SORRY

'FLU

DINNER

BATH

JUNE

"THE BEANO"

£1.25

185 Fleet Street, London, EC4A 2HS.

The kids come in, without a din.

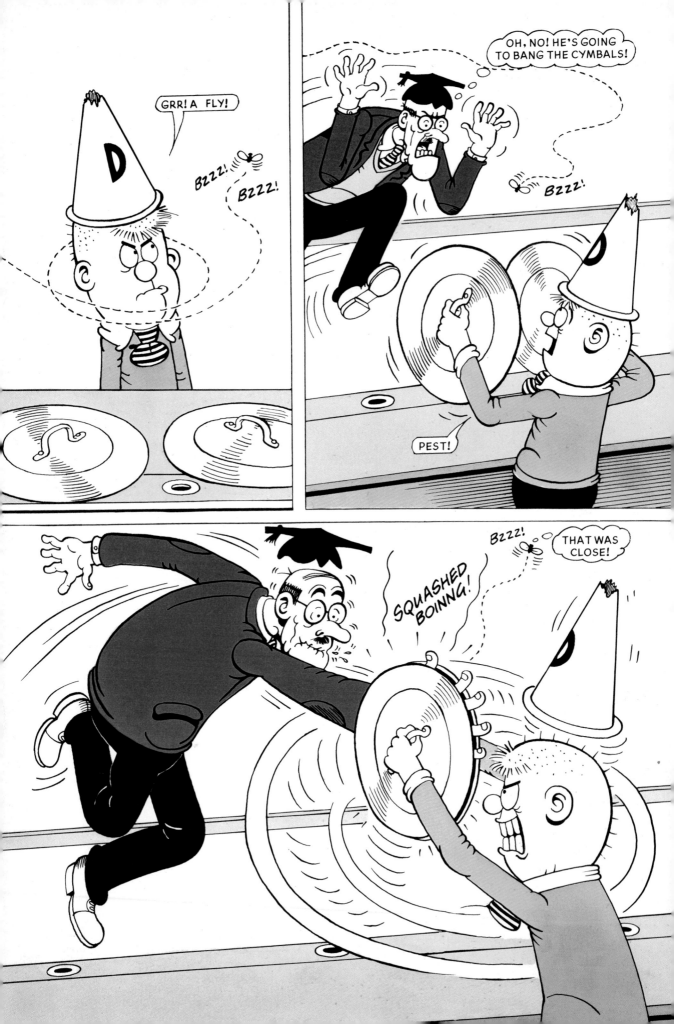

Here comes Head, seeing red!

ROGER the

DODGER

This dodge lets you see what's on TV!

Wet Dad—too bad!

A cosy chat? Can't have that!

What a place to put your face!

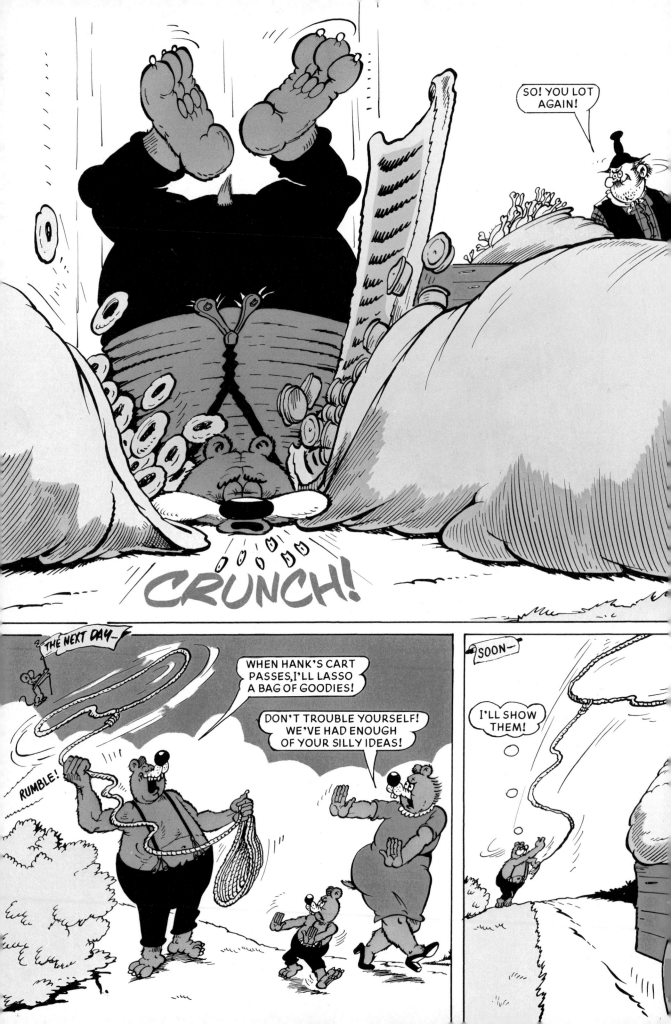

LUMBERJACK

Heading for trouble at the double!

How to go fast on snow!

PLUM'S IN TOWN

YOUR INDIAN PAL VISITS LONDON

The Fix-it Twins

Chips and fish is not Plum's dish!

Tell your friends about "THE BEANO"!

NEVER BE WITHOUT A "BEANO"!

If I were a

What's in a name?

N IS FOR HIS **N**IBS, OUR LEADER BRAVE AND GOOD—

I IS FOR **I**DEAS HE HAS FOR PINCHING FOOD!

BUT WHISKERS, HIS PET PUSSY-CAT, IS NEVER FAR **B**EHIND!

THUMP!

L IS FOR THE **L**ARDER IN PORTLY PORKY'S **L**OBBY—

R IS FOR **R**ETURNING WITH THE GOODIES FOR OUR TREAT—

How absurd—there's no such word!

See below—horses of snow!

Sue will get the last laugh yet!

SHEEP DOG

They're not much good at working with wood!

BIFFO THE BEAR

*PAPER, PLEASE.

CERTAINLY, BIFFO.

WOW! IT SAYS HERE THAT THE BANK WAS ROBBED YESTERDAY...

... THE POLICE ARE ON THE ROBBER'S TRAIL AT THIS VERY MOMENT! GOSH! WHAT'S THIS...?

That old lot don't look so hot!

What a shot that player's got!

Out of puff—not fit enough!

16 Super Pages of Dennis the Menace and GNASHER

Dennis can brag—it's in the bag!

Later, at the fishing contest on the pier—

BAIT

LURES

JUDGE

WALTER'S GOT ALL THE GEAR. HE HAS EVERYTHING— BUT FISH!

YOU MUST HAVE A SMALL FISHING ROD, DENNIS!

WHO NEEDS A FISHING ROD?

I'VE GOT GNASHER!

WHAT..?

GERONIMO!

MENACE MASK

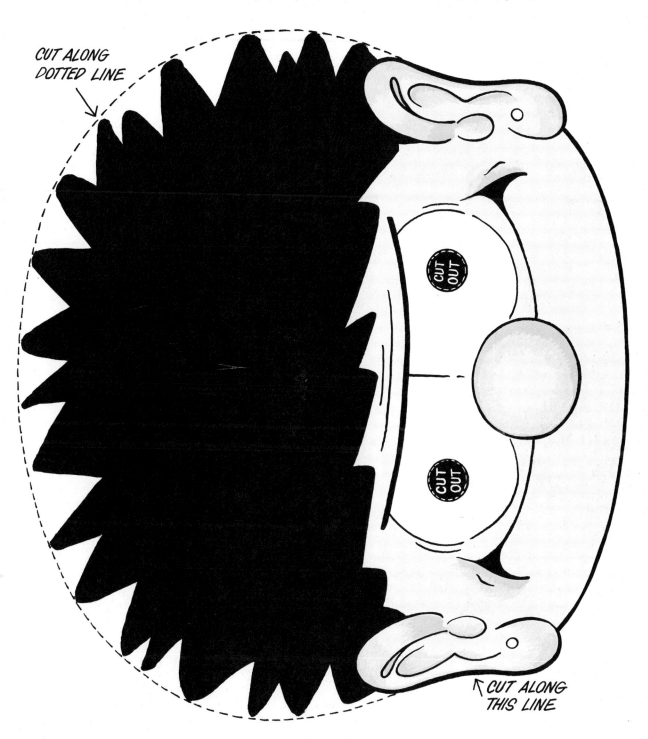

CUT ALONG DOTTED LINE

CUT OUT

CUT OUT

CUT ALONG THIS LINE

AFTER YOU'VE CUT OUT THE MASK AND THE EYE-HOLES, PIERCE SMALL HOLES IN THE EARS FOR A HEAD-BAND *(STRING OR ELASTIC).*

(P.S. THERE'S ANOTHER MASK OVER THE PAGE!)

SOFTY MASK

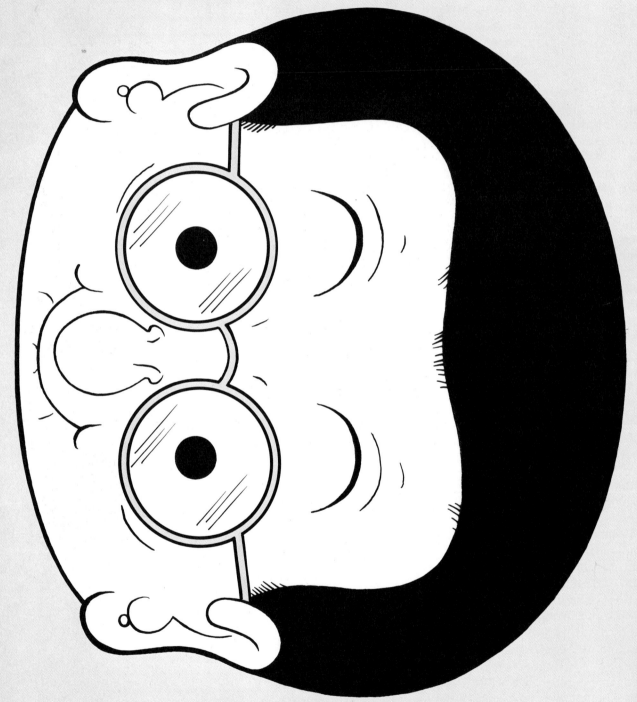

A MESSAGE FROM WALTER THE SOFTY:—
"I HOPE ANY OF MY FANS WHO DON'T WANT TO
WEAR THAT HORRIBLE MENACE MASK WILL FIND
THIS ONE MORE TO THEIR TASTE!"

Model Dog

1. STICK PICTURE ON FIRM CARDBOARD.
2. NEATLY CUT OUT THE PARTS WITH A PAIR OF SCISSORS *(CAREFULLY NOW!)*.
3. BORE HOLES IN PLACES MARKED.
4. LOOP SHORT THREADS THROUGH THE DOUBLE HOLES AND TIE PARTS TOGETHER *(NOT TOO TIGHTLY)*.
5. FIT LONG CONTROLLING THREADS TO THE OTHER HOLES IN THE TOES, TAIL, JAW AND BACK AND YOU CAN TAKE GNASHER FOR A WALK!

P.S. Read the next page first!

And so——

I SAY! HOW JOLLY INTERESTING! A GIANT, HAIRY CATERPILLAR!

OH, NO, IT'S NOT!

BULL'S-EYE!

WHACK!

YEOWCH!

And——

NOW FOR SOMETHING EQUALLY MENACING!

SPLOOSH!

BUS STOP

THERE THEY ARE! GET THE PESTS!

READY, MENACES?

AY-OOP!

HUP!

CRUMPH!

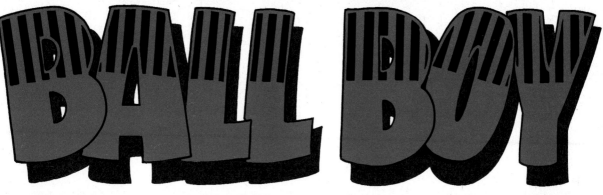

That afternoon—

LET'S TRY TO BE PERFECT PLAYERS TODAY, TEAM, AND WE'RE BOUND TO WIN TODAY'S MATCH!

WHAT ON EARTH ARE YOU WEARING THOSE FOR, TOMMY?

SORRY, B.B.—MY SHORTS ARE GETTING WASHED—THESE WERE ALL I COULD FIND!

Soon after kick-off—

OH, NO!

SOFT SHOT

DID YOU SEE THAT SOFT GOAL, TICH?

ER—NO, B.B.—MY HAIR BLEW OVER MY EYES!

Soon—

PLENTY OF TIME TO GATHER THIS PASS!

PASS

But—

WHY DIDN'T YOU WARN ME ABOUT THAT FAST WINGER, TUBBY?

MMMF! MOUTH FULL OF—UMMF!—CHEWING GUM! CHOMP!

What a useless lot Ball Boy's got!

Never fear, the artist's here!

LORD SNOOTY

WISH WE HAD SOMETHING TO DO.

IDLE

FED UP

BORED

HEY!

BONK!

EXCUSE ME! DO YOU THINK I COULD HAVE MY BALL BACK?

GASP!

WHY CERTAINLY! HEY! THERE'S AN IDEA— LET'S HAVE A GAME OF HOCKEY—YOUR TEAM AGAINST MINE!

OK!

GOOD THINKING, SNOOTY!

The day of the match

SLURP! I'LL EAT THIS AFTER THE GAME!

STICK OF ROCK

CHARGE!

YAHOO! THIS SHOULD BE EASY! THOSE LITTLE GIRLS WON'T STAND A CHANCE!

Wow! Such grace! And see that pace!

Billy races ten quick paces!

Super-fast fun with Billy's gun!

Try as they might—not a bite!

Not a morsel to spare—it's hard to "bear"!

Minnie the Minx

FANTASTIC—HE'S MADE HIS ASSISTANT DISAPPEAR!

← THE GREAT MARVO

HUH! ANYBODY COULD DO TRICKS LIKE THAT IF HE TRIED.

IF IT'S AS EASY AS THAT, MAKE ME DISAPPEAR, LITTLE MISS KNOW-ALL!

OH—ER—WELL . . .

. . . MAKE IT WORTH MY WHILE—GIVE ME 50p TO GO TO THE PICTURES IF I SUCCEED!

DON'T KNOW HOW I'D MANAGE TO PAY IF I'VE VANISHED, BUT IT'S A DEAL!

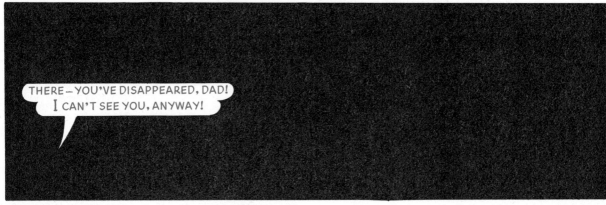

SWEET

HERE'S WHY I SOMETIMES BORROW TOYS FROM . . . .

I'LL HAVE SOME OF YOUR CHOCS, SHRIMP!

NOT IF I CAN HELP IT!

WIND

'BYE, 'BYE TOUGH GUY

Sue is playing "shops"

LET'S SCARE SUE WITH THIS WORM!

HARRIET AND MABEL— SUE'S ENEMIES

WE'LL PUT IT IN HER TILL!

OOF!

LET'S PUNCTURE SUE'S PRAM TYRES!

HELLO, LITTLE DOGGY!

TRUNDLE

CIRCUS DOG

Isn't that cute?—An armoured suit!

This is the first photograph we ever took of Porky and Whiskers...

... and this is the SECOND

(Chiseller's the photographer)

An early snapshot of Cheddar George

(Excellent likeness)

Porky used to let us play with his toys. Sometimes he even joined in!

Enor Mouse has always been pretty strong.

This is our first raid on Porky's dining table. (sorry about the shaky picture, but Sniffler was standing on a plate of orange jelly when he took it).

Photograph laugh!

Look below— the winner's on show!

Um feather wings are tickly things!

They plan to stay outside today.

An indoor pool in Bash Street School.

IT'S HANDY HAVING SNOW ON MY DESK!

LATER—

MELTING SNOW

DRIP

DRIP

YOU'LL HAVE TO LET US GO NOW! IT'S LIKE THE LOCAL SWIMMING POOL IN HERE!

STAY IN YOUR SEATS, OR ELSE!

HESITATING

WHAT'S AN "OR ELSE"?

Why so slow when it's time to go?

SLIPPER

WATER-PISTOL

ONIONS

GUILTY

KIDDING

POLICEMAN